Disney's Winnie the Pooh

Annual 2002

Editor / Designer: Lisa Carless
© Disney. Based on the Pooh stories by A.A. Milne. © The Pooh Properties Trust.
Published in Great Britain in 2001 by Egmont World, an imprint of Egmont Children's Books Ltd,
239 Kensington High Street, London, W8 6SA.
Printed in Italy. ISBN 0 7498 5145 7

£5.99
UK only

Contents

Hello, boys and girls!

Welcome to the Hundred Acre Wood with Winnie the Pooh and all his friends. Why don't you join in the fun and games? There's so much to do!

We've hidden lots of little objects throughout your annual — see how many you can find of each one and write that number in the box next to it. Have fun finding them!

Hello, from all of us!

Hello! I'm Pooh!

Hello! I'm Piglet!

Hello! I'm Roo!

Hello! I'm Christopher Robin!

Hello! I'm Owl!

6

The snow Piglet

Pooh

1 One snowy day, Christoph Robin made a *snow Piglet* an took it to show Pooh. "**Pooh!**" he cried, knocking on the door. But Pooh wasn't at hom

2 "I'll **fetch Piglet** and show it to him," thought Christopher Robin. He left the *snow Piglet* outside Pooh's door and went off to get Piglet.

fetch Piglet

Hello, Piglet

3 A few minutes later, Pooh returned and saw who he thought was Piglet on a sledge outside his door. "**Hello, Piglet!**" he cried, walking over to him.

4 Piglet didn't answer. "Have you called for me to go sledging with you?" asked Pooh, as he got closer. "**Goodness!**" he gasped. "You're covered in snow!".

Goodness

5 Now, Pooh was really worried. "Poor Piglet. He's frozen stiff in the snow," he thought, "I must take him **inside**, out of the cold."

inside

warm up

6 Pooh pulled the sledge inside his house. Then, he fetched a blanket to put around Piglet's shoulders. "You'll soon **warm up**," he said.

7 Just then, there was a knock at the door. Pooh went to answer it. Who do you think it was? "**Piglet**!" gasped Pooh, staring at Piglet and Christopher Robin.

Piglet

8 They all looked into the front room and saw that the *snow Piglet* had started to melt! "It's my **Snow Piglet**!" laughed Christopher Robin.

Snow Piglet

Silly me

9 "I brought it to show you, but you weren't in!" he explained. "**Silly me**!" laughed Pooh. He was pleased that Piglet hadn't frozen in the snow, after all.

Colour the two matching pictures in each row.

11

A snowy day rhyme

Talk about what's happening in the picture.

What colour is Eeyore's scarf?

12

What colour is snow?

Roo held on tight,
And off they sped.
Down the hill
On Tigger's sled!

"Help!" cried Eeyore,
"We're going too fast!"
Even Tigger gasped,
As they both whizzed past!

How do you like to have fun?

Can you find these things in the big picture? Tick the boxes when you see them.

13

Tigger's surprise

Here's Tigger to show you how to make a super snowman.

What you need: A small cardboard tube, some cotton wool, some paste, some coloured paper, round-ended scissors and a small piece of material.

1 First, cover the cardboard tube with paste and then wrap a layer of cotton wool around it.

2 Then, roll a ball of cotton wool for the snowman's head and paste it on to the top of the tube.

4 Finally, make your snowman a scarf from a scrap of material.

3 Now, cut out some eyes, a nose and a mouth from the coloured paper and paste them in place on the snowman's head.

Owl's puzzle page

Which of these would warm you up and which would cool you down?

Pooh's nature notes

Hello, everyone. I'm going to tell you all about otters.

Otters live by rivers and canals or the coast. They have long tails, brown waterproof fur and webbed feet.

I'm very shy!

What colour is the otter's fur?

Point to the otter in the river.

Otters spend most of their time on land. They dive underwater to catch fish then bring them on land to eat.

I'm a brilliant swimmer!

Do you like fish?

Mummy otters make a safe den away from the river for their cubs so they don't drown. The cubs don't swim until they are about three months old.

How many cubs can you see?

Piglet's colouring pages

Colour this picture with your pens, paints or crayons.
Look at the little picture to see which colours to use.

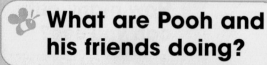

What are Pooh and his friends doing?

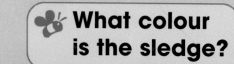

What colour is the sledge?

How many birds can you see?

Have you ever built a snowman?

19

Roo's boots

"Are you sitting comfortably, Pooh?" asked Christopher Robin. "Then, I'll tell you a little story about you and some of your friends..."

Owl asked all his friends to come to his house after lunch. "And don't forget your Wellington Boots," he said. "I wonder why we need our wellies?" said Piglet, as he and Pooh made their way to Owl's house. "It isn't even raining now." "Maybe we're going to splash in puddles," said Pooh. "Ah! There you are, Pooh, and Piglet, too," smiled Owl. "All we need is Roo, then we can start our welly throwing contest." "Welly throwing contest?" asked Pooh, puzzled. Owl explained that they all had to throw a welly as far as they could. "The one who throws their welly the furthest distance, is the winner," he said with a little smile. Everyone thought that sounded like fun. They waited eagerly for Roo to arrive so they could start the game. But there was no sign of him. "We'll start without him," said Rabbit. "He can join in when he arrives." So everyone lined up with their wellies. Tigger threw his welly first. It landed just in front of the tree. "Very good," said Owl. Then Pooh threw his welly but it

went over his shoulder and just missed Piglet! Rabbit's welly flew past Tigger's welly and landed by a bush. "I'm going to win!" he boasted. Then Roo came running along, wearing an enormous pair of Wellingtons. "Sorry I'm late. I couldn't find my boots, so mummy lent me hers," he panted. But his boots were so big, Roo tripped up in them. One of the wellies shot off his foot, whizzed through the air and landed way past the others. "Well, I never! Roo's the winner!" declared Owl. Everyone cheered. "Well done, Roo," said Rabbit. "It's a good thing I couldn't find my wellies, after all," smiled Roo. "I'd never have won the game, otherwise!"

"Did Roo find his wellies in the end?" asked Pooh. "Oh, yes, Kanga brought them along, then you all had a lovely time splashing in puddles." "I'll bet we were tired after that!" yawned Pooh. "I'm tired, too. I'm going to sleep now. Goodnight." "Goodnight, Pooh Bear."

Rabbit's maze

Can you work out which skipping rope Rabbit needs to follow to get home?

In training

1 Pooh went to visit Rabbit and was surprised to find him skipping. "**Skipping** is one of the best ways of getting fit," Rabbit told him.

2 "I'm making sure I'm the **fittest** for the keep-fit competition this afternoon," said Rabbit. But Rabbit wasn't very good at skipping!

3 He kept getting tangled up in the rope and tripping up. "This **silly rope** is hopeless!" he grumbled. "I can't skip properly with it."

Like this

4 "If you hold your arms out a bit wider, you won't get tangled up in the rope," said Pooh. "**Like this**?" asked Rabbit, trying again.

Sorry, Pooh

5 But Pooh was standing too close! "**Sorry, Pooh!**" laughed Rabbit.

Help

6 Then the rope got caught on the branch of a tree. The branch sprang back, pulling the rope and Rabbit with it. "**Help!**" he cried.

7 Rabbit swung back and forth from the branch. "Get me **down**!" he shouted to Pooh.

8 "How?" asked Pooh. Then, Pooh had an idea. "**I'll pull** you down," he said. He grabbed hold of Rabbit's legs and pulled hard. "Be careful!" cried Rabbit.

9 Then suddenly, the rope broke and Rabbit came tumbling down, right on top of Pooh! "**Thanks**, Pooh!" said Rabbit. "Glad to help!" gasped Pooh.

Keeping fit rhyme

Who is the fittest,
Rabbit or Tigger?
Who can do press-ups,
Better and quicker?

What colour is Tigger?

What is happening in the picture?

They're both training,
To see who's the best,
But it's such hard work,
They soon need a rest!

Who do you think is the
fittest, Tigger or Rabbit?

Can you find
these things
in the big
picture? Tick
the boxes
when you
see them.

Can you think of any other
exercises they can do?

27

Piglet's colouring pages

**Colour this picture with your pens or pencils.
Look at the little picture to see
which colours to use.**

Who can you see in the picture?

How many flowers can you see?

28

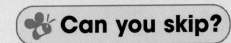
What colour is the grass?

Can you skip?

The kite

1 One morning, Pooh was outside cleaning his windows when he thought he saw someone's reflection in the window. Someone with a funny-shaped face!

2 "Hello," said Pooh. He turned around and saw a kite! It was bobbing about on a long piece of string.

3 Christopher Robin was holding the other end of the string. "Can you throw my kite back up in the air, please?" he shouted to Pooh.

4 Pooh threw the kite in the air, but kept hold of its tail. Then, a big gust of wind blew him up in the air, too!

5 "Oh, dear, I don't think Pooh Bears are meant to fly!" thought Pooh. He held on tightly to the kite tail.

6 "I hope I don't bump into a tree," cried Pooh. "Hold on, Pooh, I'll get you down," cried Christopher Robin.

7 Just then, Roo came along. "Can I have a turn at flying Pooh?" he asked. "I'm trying to *unfly* him," replied Christopher Robin.

8 Suddenly, the wind dropped and Pooh stopped flying a bit sooner than everyone expected.

9 "Don't worry, Pooh, I'll catch you!" cried Christopher Robin. He and Roo ran after Pooh. Do you think they will catch him?

32

10 "Got you!" laughed Christopher Robin, as Pooh fell into his arms. "What's it like to fly, Pooh?" asked Roo.

11 "It's a bit scary," said Pooh. "I'm glad I'm not a kite." "So am I," said Christopher Robin. "I like you being Pooh."

Piglet's drawing

Can you help Piglet finish this picture of a kite by drawing on a pretty pattern?

Owl's counting page

How many red balloons can you count?

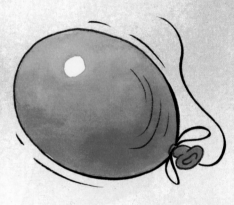

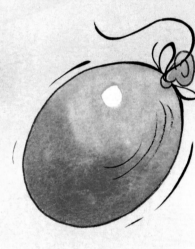

Is there one yellow balloon or are there two?

Are there more red balloons than blue?

Rabbit's maze

Can you tell which kite Rabbit is holding?
What shape is on that kite?

36

Tigger's surprise

Here's Tigger to show you how to make a super greetings card for a special friend. All you need is some card and some crayons.

1 Fold the card in half, like this, and draw on a pretty picture.

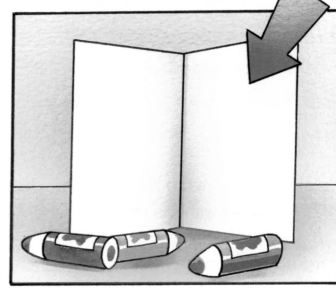

2 Then open it up.

3 Copy this message inside. But remember to add your friend's name and your own.

TO

THANK YOU FOR BEING MY FRIEND LOVE FROM

The balloon monster

"Are you sitting comfortably, Pooh?" asked Christopher Robin. "Then I'll tell you what happened when Piglet and Pooh took their balloon for a walk..."

Piglet and Pooh were walking past Rabbit's house with their balloon when they saw him running around the garden, chasing the crows away from his vegetable patch. "And don't come back!" he yelled, as the crows flew off. Then Rabbit noticed Piglet and Pooh watching him. "Those pesky crows keep eating the seeds I've just planted," he told them. "I've been chasing them away all morning." "I've got an idea to keep the crows away," said Piglet. "We can make a balloon monster with our balloon." Piglet drew a face on the

alloon, tied it to a stick in the garden
nd draped a coat around it. When the
rows saw it they were so scared they flew
way again. Rabbit was so pleased he
sked Piglet and Pooh to join him for
nch. "I don't think I'll have any more
ouble with those crows now, thanks to
ur balloon monster," he said happily.
hen Pooh and Piglet set off home, they
oticed that the balloon monster's coat
as falling off the stick. Pooh tried to put it
ack on again but accidentally poked
e balloon with the stick. It burst with a
ud BANG. The terrified crows flew out of
e tree and off into the wood,
uawking loudly. "Sorry, Rabbit!"
id Pooh. "Now I've ruined
ur balloon monster."
hat's okay," laughed
abbit. "That bang gave
e crows such a fright
on't think they'll come
ack in a hurry!"

"Did the crows come back?"
asked Pooh. "No, they decided
the balloon monster was much
too scary so they went to find
their food from somewhere
else," said Christopher Robin.
"Oh, good," said Pooh. "Well,
goodnight. I'm going to sleep
now." "Goodnight, Pooh Bear."

39

Owl's picture

1 "It's a friendly day today," Pooh thought to himself. "Just the sort of day to share with a friend." Then along came Piglet.

2 "Hello, Pooh," said Piglet. "I thought today was just the sort of day for visiting friends." "So it is," agreed Pooh. "I'll come with you."

3 First, Piglet and Pooh visited Rabbit. He was dusting a big picture. "Owl wants this so I'm cleaning it up for him," said Rabbit.

4 "We'll take it to him," offered Pooh. So Piglet and Pooh carried the picture to Owl's house. "It's a **very** big picture," gasped Piglet. "And very heavy!" grunted Pooh. Suddenly, Pooh tripped…

5 …and the picture fell straight on to Piglet, making a *Piglet Picture*! "Oh, dear," said Piglet. "Look what's happened to the picture!"

6 Pooh helped Piglet out of the picture. "I don't think Owl will want a picture with a Piglet hole in the middle," sighed Piglet.

7 Then Pooh had an idea. "Let's paint another picture for Owl," he said. So Piglet fetched some potted flowers for both of them to copy.

8 When Piglet and Pooh had finished their painting, they pasted it over the ripped picture in the frame. "Now that looks nice!" Pooh said, proudly.

9 Piglet and Pooh carefully carried the picture to Owl's house. "Rabbit sent you this," said Pooh. But then the picture started to peel off!

10 "Oh, dear," said Piglet and Pooh, who then explained to Owl what had happened. "Never mind," smiled Owl. "I only wanted the frame...

11 ... for this picture of my Uncle Ossie!" "Oh, good," said Pooh. "We can give our painting to Rabbit as a present!"

Piglet's drawing

Can you help Piglet to finish his drawing of a bottle? Then, you could colour it in.

Rabbit's maze

Can you help Rabbit to put his clothes away? With your finger, trace a path through the maze to his chest of drawers.

How many red bottles can you count?

Count the notes.

Are there one or two green bottles?

The missing whistle

1 Piglet went to see Rabbit. "**Come in!**" Rabbit called. Piglet tried to go in, but he couldn't open the door.

2 Piglet pushed and pushed. At last the door opened and he fell inside. "What a **mess!**" he said, looking around.

3 Rabbit was searching through a drawer. "I've lost my **whistle**," he told Piglet. "I had it this morning but I can't find it now!"

4 "**I'll help** you look for it," offered Piglet. So Piglet looked under the table and under the stools while Rabbit searched through the cupboards.

5 "**Bother**! I can't find it anywhere!" grumbled Rabbit. When he turned around he couldn't find Piglet, either! Do you know where Piglet is?

6 "I'm **here**!" said Piglet, scrambling out of the pile of things Rabbit had thrown over him. "I didn't find the whistle," he said.

7 "Well, we'd better **tidy up** now and have some tea," said Rabbit. He picked everything up and put it in the cupboard – even Piglet!

8 Rabbit fetched a pot of stew he'd made for tea. "That smells **nice**!" said Piglet, climbing out of the cupboard.

9 Rabbit was eating the stew when he bit on something hard. "**My whistle**!" he gasped. "It was hiding in the stew all the time!" laughed Piglet.

Join the fun and games in...

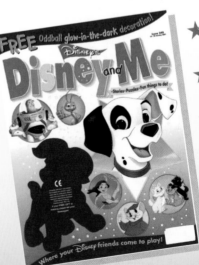

WIN A FANTASTIC FAMILY BREAK TO

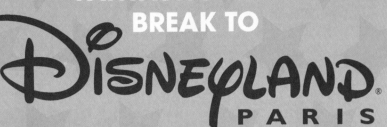

Disneyland
PARIS

Visitors young and old can discover the magic of Disneyland® Paris with its Theme Park, its seven themed hotels and of course Disney® Village, the entertainment centre.

The prize:

Includes two nights bed and breakfast for a family of four in a family room (two double beds) at one of the fabulous Disneyland Paris themed hotels, plus three days unlimited entry into the Disneyland Park. And what a time to go!

Disneyland® Paris 2002

From January through March 2002, Kids Go Free to the Magic with Disneyland Paris. Celebrate a world-wide carnival of colours and traditions with all our Disney friends on floats, storeys high with the ImagiNations Parade. Summer nights last longer with our Magical Summer Evenings. Main Street Electrical Parade presents a fairyland of lights and illuminations. To top it all, there's the Tinker Bell's, Fantasy in the Sky Fireworks, right beside Sleeping Beauty's Castle. In October, come along and enjoy our hair-raising month-long Hallowe'en Festival - it's terror-ific. Then, go BOOM! with the Bonfire Night Spectacular in November where the skies light up and see our amazing floating bonfire on Lake Disney®. Then, before you know it, you can celebrate the Christmas Season Disney-style and have a Very Merry Disney® Christmas all wrapped up for you!

Disneyland® Paris. Come and live the magic.
**For more information or a free brochure, call: 08705 030303
or visit: www.disneylandparis.com**

To enter, answer this simple Disney question: *Name Simba's uncle in the Lion King.*

Send your answer, along with your name and address to:
Egmont Children's Books Ltd, Unit 7, Millbank House, Riverside Park, Bollin Walk, Wilmslow, Cheshire, SK9 1BJ.

The closing date for entries is the 12th January 2002.

Spring rhyme

Tidying the garden

Is something we should do.

It won't take long, it's lots of fun,

With friends like Tigger and Pooh.

● What colour is the hosepipe?

Can you find these things in the picture? Put a tick in the box when you have found each one.

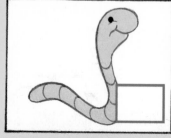

● Do you have a shed in your garden?

They went to find some tools,

Pooh opened the shed door wide,

But when they went in, things went a bit dim,

And then they were shut inside!

● How many flower pots can you see?

55

Piglet's colouring pages

Colour this picture with your crayons or pens. Look at the little picture to see which colours to use.

HOME SWEET HOME

Who can you see in the picture?

56

What colour is the wardrobe?

● **What has happened to Roo's quilt?**

● **How many feathers can you see?**

Tidying the garden

1 One day, Tigger saw Pooh in the garden. "Hello, Tigger. I'm tidying the garden ready for spring," said Pooh. "That sounds fun," said Tigger. "I'll help you."

2 "Thank you," said Pooh. He and Tigger went into the shed to get the wheelbarrow. All of a sudden, the door sprang shut and they couldn't open it again.

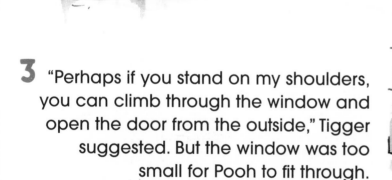

3 "Perhaps if you stand on my shoulders, you can climb through the window and open the door from the outside," Tigger suggested. But the window was too small for Pooh to fit through.

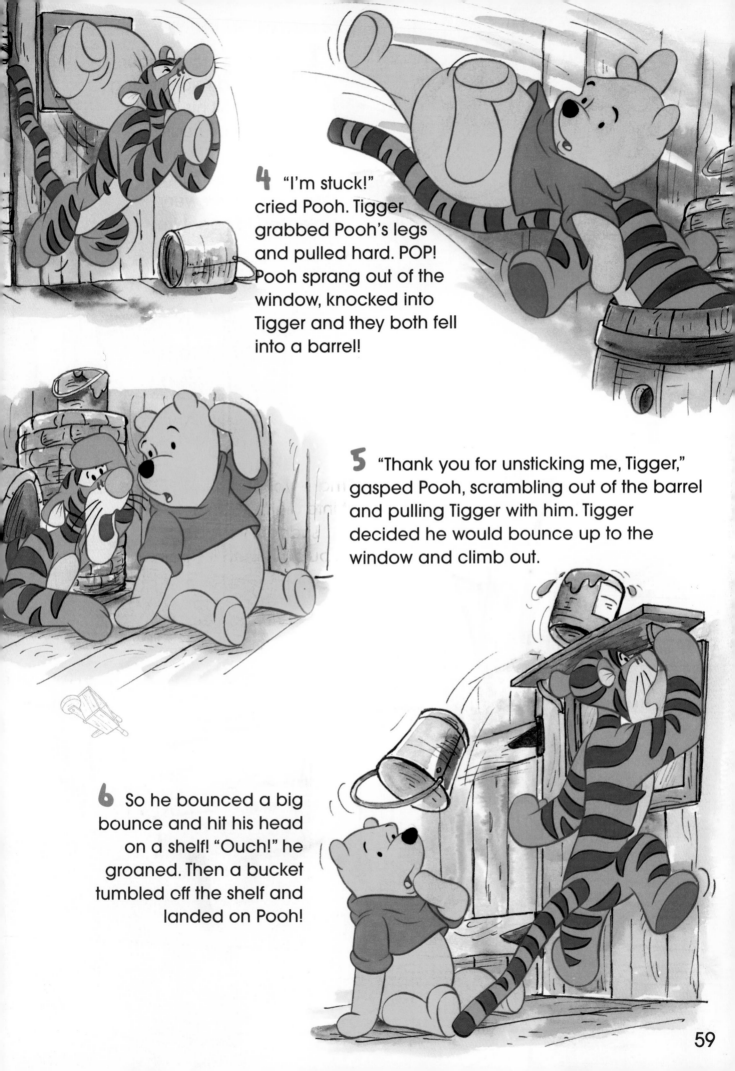

4 "I'm stuck!" cried Pooh. Tigger grabbed Pooh's legs and pulled hard. POP! Pooh sprang out of the window, knocked into Tigger and they both fell into a barrel!

5 "Thank you for unsticking me, Tigger," gasped Pooh, scrambling out of the barrel and pulling Tigger with him. Tigger decided he would bounce up to the window and climb out.

6 So he bounced a big bounce and hit his head on a shelf! "Ouch!" he groaned. Then a bucket tumbled off the shelf and landed on Pooh!

7 "I missed," said Tigger. "I know," said Pooh, taking the bucket off his head. Just then, they heard Piglet's voice. "Pooh! Where are you?" Tigger and Pooh were very pleased to hear him!

8 "Help, Piglet! We're in the shed!" they both shouted as loud as they could. "That sounds like Tigger and Pooh," said Piglet, opening the shed door.

9 "Hello!" said Piglet. "Don't shut the door!" cried Tigger, running towards it. But it was too late! "Now we're a trapped," sighed Pooh.

10 "Yes, but Piglet's small enough to climb through the window," said Tigger. "W-what w-window?" asked Piglet, nervously. "This one," said Tigger, lifting Piglet up on to his shoulders.

11 Piglet climbed out of the window, walked around and opened the shed door again. He held it open as Tigger and Pooh ran out. "Well done, Piglet!" said Pooh.

12 "Oh, no! We've left the wheelbarrow in the shed," remembered Tigger. "No, you haven't," said Piglet. "I borrowed it earlier. I've just brought it back to you. Look!" Pooh was pleased.